To My Wished-For Grandchildren
Te Querré Por Siempre Más Un Dia
(I Will Love You Forever And A Day)

Library of Congress Control Number: 2012948671
ISBN: 978-0-615-69268-5

10 9 8 7 6 5 4 3 2 1

Printed in the United States of America
First Edition

Alemar Publishing
PO Box 913
Mill Valley, California 94942-0913
www.alemarpublishing.com

Produced by SupperTime Entertainment

WISHES

Written by Claudia Trinklein-Engman

Illustrated by
Chris Hill

for
Annadel
&
Henry —

Happy wishing!

Claudia Trinklein-Engman
2013

Chris Hill

Alemar Publishing

Both my mother and my grandmother made making wishes fun and a part of my growing up. It was a rapid-fire link to magical thinking and playful fantasies.

One is never too old to believe in magic or the power of hope.

If the very first words you say on the first day of a new month are "WHITE RABBIT" you get to make a wish... This is so hard to remember!

Keep looking—there are wish possibilities EVERYWHERE!

When you look at your clock: If the numbers are the same, you can make your wish.

You can wish on a car that has only one shining headlight... as kids, we called it a "PADIDDLE."

For really important things... you may need to wish more than once...

¡Ten Paciencia Por Favor!

When you cross a railroad track, hold your feet up and make a wish! Nietos: Railroad crossing—look out for the cars.

Can you spell that without any R's?

P.S. I can!

If you hold your breath across a bridge, you can wish for something extra special.

(It works in a tunnel, too!)

Anytime you see a
bride, you get to make
your very special wish…

Never, never wish for something bad or mean!
Me Gustan Los Deseos.

Make a wish on your balloon...
the helium kind... And let it go!

Solo Un Deseo A La Vez... No fair wishing for a thousand wishes!

On your birthday, make a wish before
you blow out all the candles!
Happy Birthday to you!
"¡Feliz Cumpleaños A Ti!"

And if it's not your birthday, put your ring around one of the candles before they are lit.

When the birthday person blows out the candles, you can get a wish too!

Anything you eat that is shaped like a triangle...
eat the tip of the triangle last and wish hard.
The famous wish bite!

Drink all the bubbles in your milk
before they break...
Drink fast and make a wish.
Las Burbujas Son Divertidas.

After a turkey dinner, ask politely for the wishbone, let it dry out and find someone to pull one side while you pull the other.

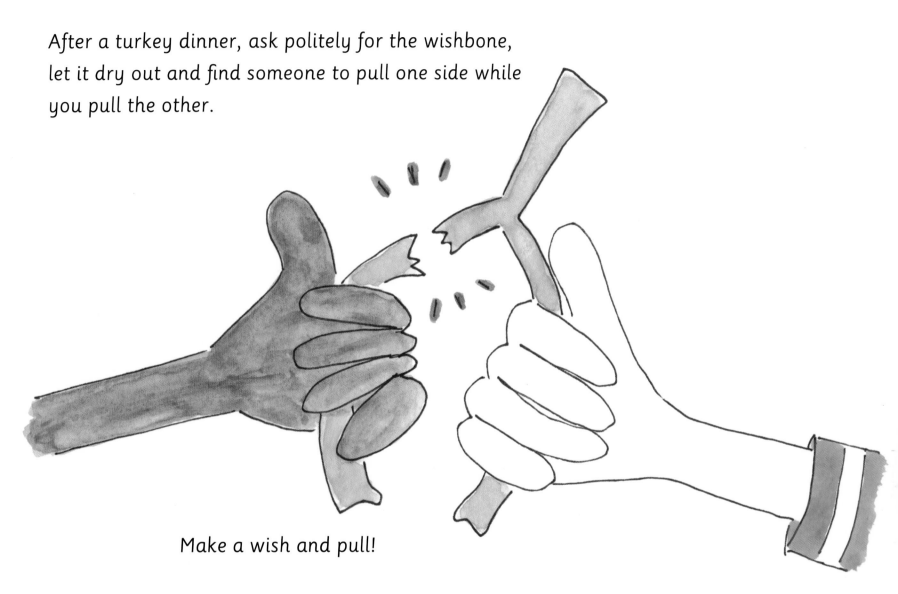

Make a wish and pull!

Whoever has the longer piece gets the wish!

If a ladybug lands on your
hand, wish hard!
That is VERY lucky!

When dandelions go to seed… blow
all the white seedlings into the wind.

¡Soplen Niños, Soplen!

Wish on a white horse
(of course.)

#1 Spot one!

#2 Lick one of your
thumbs.

#3 Press that thumb into the
palm of your other hand.

#4 Stamp that spot
with your fist.

Throw coins in a wishing well or fountain.
Don't ever tell your wish out loud because the wish
might not happen!

¡Lo Siento!

If you are lucky enough to catch a feather... make a wish.

¡Mira, Una Pluma!

Kiss the clasp on your necklace
(only if it is in the front.)
Make a wish!

¡Haz Un Deseo!

If your friend has an eyelash on her cheek and can guess which cheek...

You helped your friend get her wish!

¡Maravilloso!

If you are playing a card game that wants you and other players to put a total of four cards on the table and they are all of the same suit...

SLAP the four cards and everyone who SLAPS gets a wish!

Todas Las Personas Pueden Jugar
Y Hacer Un Deseo.

Wish on the first star you see in the sky.

"Star light, star bright
First star I see tonight
I wish I may, I wish I might
Have the wish I wish tonight"

Do you think you can make all these wishes sometime?

¡Que Tengas Una Aventura Fantástica!

GLOSSARY

Te Querré Por Siempre Más Un Dia	I Will Love You Forever And A Day
¡Ten Paciencia Por Favor!	Be Patient!
Nietos	Grandchildren
Me Gustan Los Deseos	I Like Wishes
Solo Un Deseo A La Vez	Only One Wish At A Time
"¡Feliz Cumpleaños A Ti!"	Happy Birthday To You!
Las Burbujas Son Divertidas	Bubbles Are Fun
¡Soplen Niños, Soplen!	Blow Children, Blow!
¡Lo Siento!	Sorry!
¡Mira, Una Pluma!	Look, A Feather!
¡Haz Un Deseo!	Make A Wish!
¡Maravilloso!	Wonderful!
Todas Las Personas Pueden Jugar Y Hacer Un Deseo	Everyone Can Play And Make A Wish
¡Que Tengas Una Aventura Fantástica!	Have A Fantastic Adventure!